Treasure Chest

A Beka Book® Pensacola, FL 32523-9100
an affiliated ministry of PENSACOLA CHRISTIAN COLLEGE®

To parents and teachers:

Treasure Chest is an appealing collection of stories and poetry designed to build confidence and enthusiasm in reading. It includes classic children's tales that acquaint young readers with their rich literary heritage as well as some modern selections. As children read this delightful treasury, they make use of phonics sounds introduced in Phonics Charts 8 through 13.

The following Christian virtues and character traits are developed in the stories: acceptance of self and others, cheerfulness, cleanliness, contentment, helpfulness, honesty, industry, kindness, obedience, responsibility, and self-control.

Treasure Chest

Staff Credits

Editors: Delores Shimmin, Laurel Hicks
Edition Editor: Marion Hedquist
Editorial Assistant: Sandy Bazis
Designer: William Mayhew, Jr.
Cover Design: Michelle Johnson, Melissa Gerke
Production Artists: Tyler Nikkel, Tim Keenan, Thad Lund
Illustrators: Rosalie Hall, Frank Hicks, Brian Jekel

A *Beka Book,* a Christian textbook ministry affiliated with Pensacola Christian College, is designed to meet the need for Christian textbooks and teaching aids. The purpose of this publishing ministry is to help Christian schools reach children and young people for the Lord and train them in the Christian way of life.

Contents

Part One
Little and BIG

Phonics Charts 8, 9, and 10

Chart 8	Chart 9	Chart 10
thr in **thr**ee	**-ing** in point**ing**	**wh** in **wh**ale
ar in st**ar**s	**kn** in **kn**ot	**wh** in **wh**o
ch in **ch**ur**ch**	**gn** in **gn**at	**tch** in pa**tch**
or in m**or**ning	**ang** in b**ang**	**ear** in **ear**
ou in **ou**t	**ing** in k**ing**	**ear** in b**ear**
ow in **ow**l	**ong** in l**ong**	**ear** in **ear**th
ow in b**ow**l	**ung** in str**ung**	**old** in g**old**
er in v**er**se	**ank** in b**ank**	**mb** in la**mb**
ur in n**ur**se	**ink** in w**ink**	**ew** in fl**ew**
ir in b**ir**d	**onk** in h**onk**	**ew** in f**ew**
oi in c**oi**n	**unk** in tr**unk**	**-y** in rain**y**
oy in b**oy**	**wa** in **wa**sh	**-er** in bigg**er**
oo in b**oo**k	**a** in **a**dopt	**-est** in bigg**est**
oo in t**oo**th	**y** in bab**y**	**-ly** in slow**ly**
wor in **wor**ms	**le** in litt**le**	**-en** in sharp**en**
igh in n**igh**t	**-ed** in want**ed**	**-es** in peach**es**
all in b**all**	**-ed** in look**ed**	**ild** in ch**ild**
alk in w**alk**	**-ed** in play**ed**	**ind** in k**ind**

Part Two
Wonders Real and Fanciful

Phonics Chart 11

o in shovel	**ey** in key
a in banana	**ey** in obey
c in city	**ph** in phone
au in faucet	**ch** in chorus
aw in saw	**ought** in thought
ea in leaf	**aught** in caught
ea in thread.	**g** in giant
ea in steak	**dge** in fudge
ie in brownie	

Part Three
Pearls of Wisdom

Phonics Chart 12

a- in **a**sleep   **air** in h**air**

al- in **al**so   **u** in p**u**sh

be- in **be**cause   **ough** in en**ough**

en- in **en**joy   **ou** in c**ou**ntry

un- in **un**button   **arr** in c**arr**y

wr in **wr**inkle   **ire** in f**ire**

ould in c**ould**

Part Four

Apples, Cherries, and Pets

Phonics Chart 13

-ful in beauti**ful**   **sion** in mis**sion**ary
are in c**are**   **sion** in televi**sion**
tain in moun**tain**   **eigh** in **eigh**t
ure in p**ure**   **or** in sail**or**
ture in pas**ture**   **ar** in doll**ar**
war in **war**m   **y** in cr**y**stal
tion in na**tion**   **err** in ch**err**y

Part Five

Riddles and Giggles

Part One
Little and BIG

Jay Goes Sailing

Jay likes to make toy boats. He cuts the boats and then nails on the masts.

One day Jay made a blue and white boat. "This boat needs a red sail," he said to himself. "I will ask Mom for cloth to make the sail."

"Thank you, Mom," Jay said as his mother gave him some red cloth.

 Words to watch for:

| toy | clouds | floated | white |

Jay ran to the stream to sail his boat. He tied a rope to his blue and white boat. He held the rope in his hand as his boat floated on the water. "I need a dock," said Jay. "Then I can tie up my boat and let it float in the breeze."

With three bricks, Jay made a dock for his boat at the side of the stream. Then he tied his boat to the dock. "It floats! It floats!" cried Jay as the breeze hit the sail.

Jay lay on the grass near the stream. He looked up at the clouds in the sky. He looked at his boat as it floated on the stream. Then Jay went to sleep. . . .

—*Coletta Morrow*

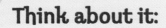

Think about it:

What did Jay do while he slept?

The Stars

Tonight I looked up in the sky
    To see what I could see,
And there I saw a million stars
    All looking down at me.

So then I looked into a pool
    To see what I could see,
And do you know, I saw more stars
    All looking up at me!

—*Pauline Croll*

Little Wind

Little wind, blow on the hilltop,
Little wind, blow on the plain,
Little wind, blow up the sunshine,
Little wind, blow off the rain.

For, lo, He that formeth the mountains,
and createth the wind . . . The Lord, The
God of hosts, is His name.

—*Amos 4:13*

The Swim Meet

Jonathan likes to swim.
He has a stream near his
home that he can swim
in. The frogs hop out as
Jonathan dives in.

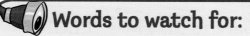

Words to watch for:

pool   boys   noise   joined   pointed

One time a frog hopped into the stream just as Jonathan swam up to breathe. The frog landed right on top of Jonathan's head! Jonathan giggled as he swam on down the stream.

The frog leaped back to the grass. PLOP!

One day Jonathan saw a note that told of a swim meet to be held at the town pool. "If I go to the swim meet," Jonathan said to himself, "I may win a prize!"

At last the day of the swim meet came. The sun shone bright in the sky. A lot of people had come to the pool to watch the swimming.

At one o'clock Jonathan joined the other swimmers at the town swimming pool.

A man had the swimmers form a line at one side of the pool. "You must swim to the far side of the pool," he said as he pointed across the pool.

BANG! The man shot his gun into the air. The boys dived into the pool.

Jonathan swam fast. He could hear the noise of the people yelling. As he got to the far side of the pool, he saw some of his friends.

"You won, Jonathan!" cried his friends. "You won!" Jonathan climbed out of the pool with a big grin.

For winning first prize, Jonathan was given a free pass to the pool, a toy airplane to fly at home, and a big blue ribbon!

—*Coletta Morrow*

Think about it:

Tell what happened first, second, third, and last.

- Jonathan saw the note.
- Jonathan won the prize.
- Jonathan swam in the pool.
- Jonathan swam in the stream.

A Close Call

One day Mazie Mouse peeked out of her little hole in the wall just in time to see Tom Cat go out the screen door.

"Oh, good!" thought Mazie. "Now I can hunt for some food to eat. Tom Cat is not here to chase me back into my hole."

 Words to watch for:
too   food   soon   good   looked   door

Mazie hurried to the table. Up the leg of the table she skittered, right to the top.

"Yum, yum," said Mazie as she nibbled some good food. "What fun it will be to eat just as much as I wish!"

Mazie Mouse ate and ate and ate—until she could eat no more. She ate ham. She ate cheese. She ate corn, peas, beans, and pudding. She ate cake. Then down the table leg she went. She waddled back to her hole in the wall.

"My, that tasted good!" sighed Mazie as she lay down on her tiny mouse-sized bed. Soon she was fast asleep.

When Mazie woke up, she let out a huge moan. She hurt all

the way from the end of her nose to the tip of her tail. "I think I ate too much food," groaned Mazie. "It was not wise to eat so much. Maybe I will feel better if I take a little walk."

As Mazie crept out of the hole in the wall, she did not see Tom Cat sitting on the rug.

Mazie walked slowly to the door. Then she heard a sound. As she turned to look, she saw Tom Cat creeping after her.

She scampered out the door with Tom Cat right behind her! Mazie ran as fast as she could to a hole in the porch. She made it to the hole just as Tom Cat pounced!

As Mazie lay panting in the hole, she could see Tom Cat trying to reach his paw into the hole.

"That was close," sighed Mazie. "Next time I will not eat all that I wish, or Tom Cat just might eat ME!"

—*Coletta Morrow*

Think about it:

Why did Mazie think she could eat all she wanted? Was she right?

Dirt, Dirt, and More Dirt

One morning Timothy walked home from the store with his mother. After he took the bag into the house, he went to the back yard to play with his dog. That was when he saw it!

Toot had dug a deep hole by the house. She had dirt from the tip of her nose to the tip of her tail!

 Words to watch for:

for   morning   work   worse

"You are a mess!" Timothy cried. "You must have a bath!"

Timothy went quickly to his room and changed into work clothes. Then he got the soap and Toot's brush and went back outside. "This will be fun," he thought.

Timothy used the hose to fill the pail with water. "Here, Toot," he called. "It's time for your bath."

Toot slowly walked toward Timothy. She had her tail down and her ears laid back.

"Lie down so I can wash you," Timothy said as he picked up the soap and brush.

Toot lay on the ground while Timothy scrubbed and scrubbed.

Timothy turned on the hose to rinse off the soap. "Now you are clean," he said as he gave Toot one last spray.

When Timothy took a rag to dry Toot, she shook and shook. Timothy got all wet! Then Toot ran around Timothy as if to say, "I got you, but you cannot get me."

"I *will* get you," called Timothy. But as he chased

Toot, he fell into the big hole that Toot had dug. Now Timothy had dirt from the top of his head to the tip of his toes.

Just then Mother saw Timothy. "You look worse than Toot did," she laughed. "Go and take a bath."

Timothy giggled as he marched into the house. Now it was his turn to get clean.

—*Coletta Morrow*

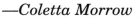

Think about it:

Tell what happened first, second, third, and fourth.

- Toot got Timothy wet.
- Toot dug a hole and got dirty.
- Timothy fell into the hole.
- Timothy got Toot wet.

Jesus Bids Us Shine

Jesus bids us shine,
  With a clear, pure light,
Like a little candle
  Burning in the night;
In this world of darkness
  We must shine,
You in your small corner
  And I in mine.

Jesus bids us shine,
  First of all for Him;
Well He sees and knows it
  If our light is dim;
He looks down from Heaven,
  Sees us shine,
You in your small corner
  And I in mine.
—E. O. Excell

 Words to watch for:
first   burning   corner   world

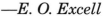

Sh-h-h!

One bright summer morning I went outside to play. I walked to Jeremy's house, but he had gone to the store.

All of the boys and girls in the houses near me were gone. Some had gone on a trip. Some had gone to camp. Some were at the beach. There was no one to play with me, and I felt sad.

As I was sitting on the ground, I thought I saw a little face peek out from the back of a tree. It looked at me—then it was gone!

Then it peeked out at me again. It was as if it said "Peek-a-boo!" I stayed very still. What was it? Would it peek out again?

I looked at the tree for a long time before I saw the little face peek out again. This time it did not go back out of sight. It slowly moved out from behind the tree.

Oh, how cute! It had two long ears, a pink nose, four legs and feet, and a round, furry tail.

I sat oh, so still. I did not want to scare that
small bunny.

The bunny hopped over closer to me—lippity,
lippity. Its pink nose felt cool as it sniffed at
my hand. "It looks so soft," I thought. "I wish I
could pet it."

As the bunny sniffed
at my knee, I carefully
reached out and touched its
soft fur.

The bunny jumped back!

I did not chase the little
bunny. I just sat still. Soon
it came back again. This
time it sniffed at my toe. It
tickled!

Then the little bunny wiggled its nose at me and hopped away.

"Leora," called Mother. "It's time for lunch."

"I saw the cutest little bunny while I was playing alone," I said to my mother. "First it played peek-a-boo with me. Then it came right up to me and sniffed at me. I must make too much noise when I play with the boys and girls."

As I ate, I thought of how sad I had been with no one to play with. But I was not sad now—I had a rabbit for a playmate!

—*Coletta Morrow*

Think about it:

Why did the rabbit come to Leora on this day and not on others?

Speck

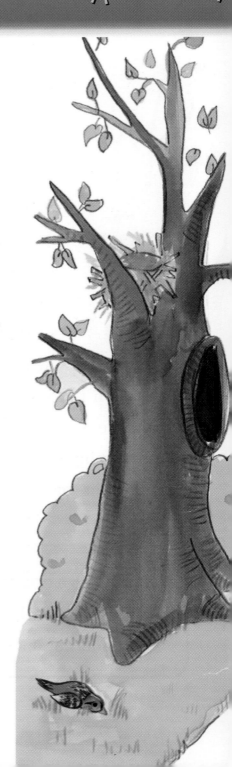

One day as Eddie and I were walking to the mall, I saw a little bird in the grass by the sidewalk. "Did it fall out of the nest?" asked Eddie.

"It looks like it," I replied. "The poor little thing! Let's help it."

Eddie and I walked over to the bird. It fluttered and flapped its wings as if it were afraid. "It's all right, little bird. We will not hurt you," I said as I knelt down beside the bird.

Words to watch for:

know   knelt   knocked

We made a small nest of grass and leaves and gently laid the bird in it. "We will be back later," Eddie told the bird. Then we hurried off to shop.

As I looked for what Mom wanted me to get, I kept thinking about the little bird. After we paid the clerk, Eddie and I ran back to the tree. "He's still here!" I called. Our little bird was huddled in the nest we had made for him.

"We cannot leave him here," panted Eddie. "Let's take him with us. I know Mom and Dad won't care." Eddie ran home and got a small box.

When Eddie returned, we got more leaves and grass and made a nest inside the box. I carefully picked up the little bird and moved him to the nest in the box. Then we carried him home.

"If he is going to be our pet for the next few days," said Eddie, "let's give him a name."

"He has a lot of little specks," I replied. "Let's call him Speck."

We took good care of Speck. We found worms for him to eat. We gave him a drink of fresh water each day. We also made sure the cat did not eat him!

In three days Speck could walk inside the box. At the end of six days he could fly. Speck flew farther and farther away, and then he was gone.

"Do you see that bird sitting over there?" I asked Eddie the next day. Eddie knocked over his bike as he hurried to look. "It must be Speck!" he cried.

Every day we watch, and every day a little bird sits on the wire by our tree. He sings to us as we play. We like to think that he is Speck.

—*Coletta Morrow*

And one of them [sparrows] shall not fall on the ground without your Father.

—*Matthew 10:29*

Three Little Kittens

The three little kittens,
They lost their mittens,
And they began to cry—
   "Oh, Mother dear,
   We sadly fear
New mittens you should buy."

"What! Buy new mittens
For my three little kittens?
I wanted to bake a pie."
   "Mew, mew,
   Mew, mew,"
The kittens began to cry.

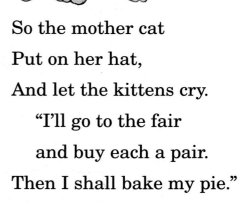

So the mother cat
Put on her hat,
And let the kittens cry.
   "I'll go to the fair
   and buy each a pair.
Then I shall bake my pie."

39

She bought some mittens
For her three little kittens
At a new fair close by.
  "Here are your mittens
  My three little kittens—
Now I shall bake my pie."

These same little kittens
Soon lost their new mittens,
And again began to cry—
  "Dear Mother, your kittens
  Have lost their new mittens
That you went to the fair to buy."

"What! Lost your mittens?
You naughty kittens—
Then you shall have no pie."
  "Mew, mew,
  Mew, mew,"
They all began to cry.

The three little kittens
Then found their mittens,
And they began to cry—
    "Oh, Mother dear,
        Our mittens are here
That you went away to buy."

"What! Found your mittens?
My dear little kittens—
Now you shall have some pie."
    "Purr, purr,
        Purr, purr,"
They all began to sigh.

The three little kittens
Put on their new mittens,
And soon ate up the pie.
    "Oh, Mother dear,
        See here, see here—"
Then they all began to cry.

"You've soiled your mittens,
You naughty kittens,"
Their Mother began to cry.
"No more new mittens
For bad little kittens—
And no more nice meat pie."

But the three little kittens
Washed their new mittens,
And hung them up to dry.
"See, your dear kittens
Have washed their mittens,"
They all began to cry.

"What! Washed your new mittens?
You dear little kittens;
But I smell a rat close by—
Hush, hush,
Hush, hush,
I'll bake another pie."

Little Mouse

One day Little Mouse came running home. "Oh, Mumsie!" he squeaked to his mother. "I just had a terrible fright!"

"Where have you been?" asked Mumsie. "What happened?"

Words to watch for:

| kind | behind | wild |
| climb | comb | told |

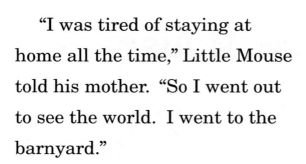

"I was tired of staying at home all the time," Little Mouse told his mother. "So I went out to see the world. I went to the barnyard."

"Oh, my poor Little Mouse," said Mumsie. "I see why you are frightened. You should never go to the barnyard by yourself. Home is the best place for a little mouse. But tell me, what frightened you?"

"At first I was not afraid, because I saw a beautiful animal that looked something like me. She was bigger than I am. She even had fur like mine, but the fur was longer."

"Oh, my!" said Mumsie. "There is no one like you in the barnyard. Tell me more. I fear I know who this animal was!"

"Well," said Little Mouse, "she lay on the grass in the sun. She looked very kind. I thought she might like to play with me, so I started to climb up and speak to her. She made a very soft sound . . . 'purrr.' "

"Oh, Little Mouse!" squeaked Mumsie. "That was a cat. You were in great danger. Cats do not like mice—they like to EAT them!"

"Did you speak to the cat?"

"No, Mumsie, I did not have a chance," said Little Mouse. "I saw a strange and dreadful-looking animal behind me."

"Who could that be?" asked Mumsie. "The cat is the most dreadful animal you could ever see. Tell me more about the dreadful-looking animal."

"Oh, Mumsie," said Little Mouse, "this animal had a long, sharp nose. His chin was red and it shook as he moved."

"A red chin?" asked Mumsie. "I know of no animal in the barnyard with a red chin. It must have been a wild beast."

"I can tell you more," Little Mouse said. "He had something red on top of his head, too. He had only two legs. Then he made a dreadful noise when he stretched out his long neck. He said, 'Cock-a-doodle-dooooo!' "

"Oh, squee-hee-hee," laughed
Mumsie. "I know what that
strange, dreadful beast was. That
was a rooster! He has a red comb
on his head and a long beak. He
will not hurt you, Little Mouse."

"But Mumsie," squeaked Little Mouse. "How shall I know which beasts will harm me and which ones won't? The cat looked so kind, and the rooster looked so dreadful!"

Mumsie gave Little Mouse a loving look. She said, "Do not speak to strange animals, my son. You cannot know what they will do by looking at them. Always remember—good deeds are better than good looks."

—Adapted from Aesop

Think about it:

How can the mother mouse's advice help you?

The Broken Wing

Winter was coming. All the birds had flown south to wait for spring. All but one. That little bird had a broken wing and could not fly very far. He had to stay behind.

The poor bird looked all around. Where could he keep warm for the winter? At last he thought of the trees in the forest.

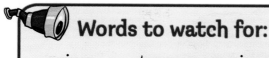

Words to watch for:

wing   strong   springtime

thank   think   drink   trunk

"Perhaps the trees will help me stay warm," thought the little bird. So he hopped into the forest. First he came to the trunk of a silver birch tree.

He looked up and asked, "Beautiful birch tree, will you let me live in your branches until springtime comes?"

The silver birch tree shook her leaves. They made a singing sound as she said, "Dear me, I have to take care of my leaves. I cannot take care of a little bird. Go away!"

So the little bird hopped along until he came to a big oak tree. "Big oak tree," said the little bird, "will you please let me live in your branches until springtime comes?"

"Oh, no!" said the big oak tree. "I cannot shelter you. I must get my new leaves ready for the spring."

The little bird hopped away dragging his broken wing until he came to a willow tree. "Oh, lovely willow tree," said the little bird, "may I live in your warm branches until springtime comes?"

The lovely willow tree waved her branches gently in the soft breeze. "Oh, no," replied the willow tree. "I cannot be bothered with you."

The poor little bird did not know where to go. He hopped along, dragging his broken wing. At last he came to a fir tree.

The fir tree saw the little bird and said, "You poor little bird. Where are you going?"

"I do not know," answered the little bird. "I cannot fly south, for I have a broken wing. I have been asking the trees to help me, but not one will give me shelter."

"You may live with me," said the fir tree. "Here is my warmest branch. Can you make it up?"

"May I live with you all winter?" asked the little bird.

"Yes," answered the fir tree. "I would like to have you stay with me."

"Thank you," chirped the little bird. "Thank you."

A tall pine tree that stood close by heard what the little bird said. "I am big and strong," said the

tall pine tree to the fir tree. "I will keep the cold wind off the little bird while he lives in your branches."

"I will give him berries to eat," said a juniper tree which stood nearby. "My berries are good for little birds."

The little bird was cared for all that winter. When the other birds returned in the spring, he could fly. His injured wing was well once again.

—*Adapted*

And be ye kind one to another.

—*Ephesians 4:32*

Part Two

Wonders Real and Fanciful

The Goldfish

I have a bowl of goldfish
    Upon my windowsill.
They're just like me, my daddy says,
    They never can keep still.

They're like the gleams of sunshine
    Which make us glad each day.
They're just like me, my mother says,
    I make her feel that way.

—Pauline Croll

Think about it:

What kind of animal would you like to be like? Why?

A Real Princess

Once upon a time a prince was looking for a princess to marry. He looked for many years. But at last he returned home without one. "I must be sure she is a *real* princess before I marry her," said the prince.

One night there was a terrible storm. The wind blew—rain poured down—lightning flashed!

Words to watch for:

prince	princess	face
once	excited	voice

In the middle of the storm someone knocked at the castle gate. "Who is out in this storm?" thought the kind old king. He quickly went down to open the gate.

A princess was standing outside the gate. She didn't look at all like a princess. Her face was wet. Her hair was blown by the wind. Water dripped from her clothes and shoes. Yet she said she was a princess.

"A real princess," thought the queen. "We shall find out."

The queen said nothing. She left quietly to make up a bed for the princess.

First she put a small dried pea on the bottom of the bed. Then she put on the mattress. She put on another mattress— and another mattress. She piled twenty mattresses on top of the pea. And on top of the twenty mattresses she piled twenty feather beds. This is where the princess was to sleep!

The next morning the prince asked the princess how she had

slept. "I did not sleep well," replied the princess. Her voice sounded tired. "I hardly closed my eyes all night long. I slept upon something very hard. I am black and blue all over."

The prince was excited. He knew then that she was a real princess! No one but a real, true princess could have felt that pea through twenty mattresses and twenty feather beds.

The prince and princess had a royal wedding—and lived happily ever after!

—*Adapted from Hans Christian Andersen*

Think about it:

Is this a true story? How do you know?

The Elephant and the Monkey

Once there lived a monkey and an elephant who could not agree. The elephant thought of himself as being very strong. How proud he was!

The monkey thought of himself as being very quick. "See how quick I am!" he chattered.

Words to watch for:

they	monkey	valley
field	believe	replied

"I believe it is better to be strong," replied the elephant. "But since we cannot agree, let's ask the wise old owl."

"We can't agree," they said to the owl. "Is it better to be strong or to be quick?"

The wise old owl said, "Do as I say, so that I may see which is better. Go to that big fruit tree in the field across the river. Pick some fruit and bring it to me."

Down the valley went the elephant and the monkey. But when they got to the river, the monkey was afraid to go across.

"I am strong," bragged the elephant. "I am not afraid of the swift water. Get on my head, and I will carry you across."

When they got to the tree on the other side of the river, they found the fruit was high above them. The elephant tried to pick the fruit with

his trunk, but it
was too high. Then he
tried to knock down the
tree, but he could not.

"I am quick," chattered the
monkey. "I will climb the tree and
drop the fruit to you."

That is just what he did. The
elephant picked up the fruit with
his trunk. The monkey hopped
onto the elephant's head,
and back across the
river they went.

"Which is better?" they asked the owl. "Is it better to be strong or to be quick?"

"Neither of you could get the fruit alone," said the owl. "It took both quickness and strength."

—*Adapted*

Think about it:

What can you do well that can help others? For what things do you need someone else's help?

Brer Fox's Tricks

Every morning Brer Bear went to the river to wash. One morning he saw Brer Fox resting under a tree.

"Brer Bear," called Brer Fox. "Let's plant a garden in this field."

"Yes, let's plant a garden," agreed Brer Bear.

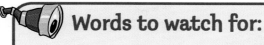

Words to watch for:

bought   brought   thought   taught

Brer Fox said, "When our garden is grown, you may have the tops. I shall have the roots."

"That is fair," replied Brer Bear. "You may have the roots, and I shall have the tops. Shall we plant corn in our garden?"

"The birds will eat corn," said Brer Fox. "Let's plant potatoes."

71

The next morning Brer Bear and Brer Fox brought potatoes to plant in their garden. They took good care of their plants.

One day Brer Bear said, "Brer Fox, our potato plants are big. The potatoes must be ready to eat."

"Fine!" said Brer Fox. "You may take the tops, and I shall take the roots."

So Brer Fox had the potatoes. Brer Bear had only the leaves.

The next spring Brer Fox said, "Brer Bear, let's plant a garden again."

"You played a trick on me last year," said Brer Bear. "But you taught me a lesson. This year you may have the tops, and I shall have the roots."

"That is fair," said Brer Fox. "This year you may have the roots. I shall have the tops."

Then Brer Fox said, "Brer Bear, what shall we plant in our garden?"

"Let's plant beets," said Brer Bear.

"The bugs will eat beets," replied Brer Fox. "Let's plant beans instead."

So Brer Fox and Brer Bear bought bean seeds to plant in their garden.

Day after day Brer Fox and Brer Bear worked in the garden. Soon the beans were large enough to eat. Brer Fox said, "Brer Bear, let us eat our beans. You may take the roots, and I shall take the tops."

So Brer Fox got the beans. Brer Bear got only the roots.

"I thought I would get food this year," said Brer Bear. "But you fooled me again. I will never plant another garden with you."

—*Adapted*

Think about it:

What did Brer Bear learn? What would have been a fair way to divide the crops?

The Little Brown Bowl

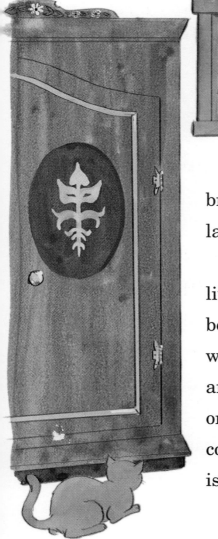

Once there was a little brown bowl that lived in a large closet with other bowls.

There were big bowls and little bowls. Some bowls had beautiful gold bands. There was a bowl that had violets around its brim. There was one bowl that was painted the colors of the sky when the sun is going down. On this bowl

was a pretty little shepherdess that wore a blue dress and hat. Her blue eyes seemed to smile all the time.

Words to watch for:

large   shepherdess   beautiful   cereal

All the bowls were beautiful except the little brown bowl. She was shy among the other bowls. She was just a plain, thick, brown bowl with not one flower.

One day the maid cleaned the closet. She set a pretty little pitcher quite close to the brown

bowl. The brown bowl asked shyly, "Why does the shepherdess always smile? Why do all the pretty bowls get to leave the closet and then come back?"

The pretty little pitcher then kindly replied, "The shepherdess smiles because she is happy. Each morning she is carried to a sunny room. There Anna eats cereal from her."

The little brown bowl was not quite so afraid now. She dared to ask, "Why doesn't someone come and get me sometimes?"

The pitcher answered politely, "They have not needed you yet. Someday they may need you. Then the little maid will come and get you."

"Shall I see Anna then?" asked the little brown bowl. Before the pitcher could reply, all the other bowls laughed.

"You will never go to see Anna!" cried the rosebud bowl. "You are too ugly to leave the closet shelf."

"Yes," added a bowl with a gold band. "Anna likes beautiful things. She would not look at you!"

As the little brown bowl sat quite still, she thought, "If only I could be beautiful, too! I wish I could go away and never come back again. No one needs me or wants me."

The little brown bowl must have been thinking out loud. The shepherdess bowl spoke softly to her, "Do not feel sad, little brown bowl. Anna does love beautiful things. But she loves useful things, too. If she ever sees you, she will love you. You must wait."

So each day passed. The pretty shepherdess bowl left each morning. When she came back, she looked brighter than when she left.

One by one the other bowls left. When they came back, they said mean things to the little brown bowl.

Then one morning the little pitcher was set on the shelf. The pitcher was quite excited. It was Anna's seventh birthday! There were seven beautiful flowers lying by her place at the table. As soon as Anna saw them, she would want something to put them in.

Oh, how each bowl desired to be chosen! "Think of the joy of holding Anna's birthday flowers!" cried the shepherdess bowl.

"Are the flowers purple?" asked the violet bowl. "With my shape and color, surely I will be chosen."

"Not one of you is fit to hold Anna's flowers," said a tall vase. "It would be just as easy for that ugly little brown bowl to be chosen."

No one had time to answer the vase. The doors to the closet swung open. The little brown bowl saw a pretty girl

with golden hair. She looked even happier than the shepherdess's smile.

Anna held her flowers and looked at the bowls. Then it happened! The little brown bowl saw Anna looking right at her.

Anna cried, "Oh, Mama, here is such a pretty little brown bowl. It is just right to hold my flowers. It is so deep and strong—it will not tip over. Why have I not found you before, little brown bowl? You shall hold flowers for me all summer!"

The little brown bowl was lifted out of the closet. Each day that summer, the little brown bowl held Anna's flowers. It stood on Anna's table.

Each morning Anna still ate her cereal from the shepherdess bowl. One morning the little brown bowl whispered to the shepherdess bowl, "Thank you for being so kind to me."

The shepherdess smiled brightly at the little brown bowl.

—*Adapted*

 Think about it:

Did Anna choose the little brown bowl because it was pretty? Why did she choose it?

Part Three
Pearls of Wisdom

Pinocchio, the Puppet-Boy

Geppetto was a woodcarver. He lived in a small room with one window. In the room stood an old chair, a bed, and a broken table.

One day Geppetto came home with a new piece of wood. He took his tools and began to carve a puppet.

"What name shall I give my puppet?" thought Geppetto as he carved. First Geppetto made the hair, then the forehead, and then the eyes. "I shall call you Pinocchio," said the kind man to the piece of wood. Then Geppetto went on with his work. He took his knife and made the nose and mouth.

 Words to watch for:

Geppetto	gently	gentleman	strange
edge	hedges	bridges	trudged

After the mouth was finished, Geppetto made the chin, the throat, the arms, and the hands. Next he carved the legs and the feet.

When Geppetto stood Pinocchio on the floor, the puppet's legs were stiff—they could not move. Geppetto held Pinocchio gently by the hand. "My little wooden son," he said, "just put one foot in front of the other."

After a few moments Pinocchio began to walk. Then he began to run. "I can run!" laughed Pinocchio. "I can run anywhere." Then Pinocchio jumped through the open window and ran down the street.

"Come back, Pinocchio!" called Geppetto.
"Come back!"

Pinocchio ran and ran. He jumped over hedges
and skipped across bridges. At last he trudged
home. The door was open. Pinocchio walked
in and locked the door. He was so tired that he
threw himself on the floor to rest.

"Cri-cri-cri," said a voice.

Pinocchio jumped to his feet. "Who is talking?"

"I am," said a cricket. "I have lived with your father, Geppetto, for a long time. He is out searching for you now. Please do not run away from him again."

"But I must leave tomorrow morning," said Pinocchio. "If I stay here I shall have to go to school. I don't want to study. It is much more fun to chase butterflies and climb trees."

"Not go to school!" replied the cricket. "You will grow up to be a perfect donkey. Everyone will make fun of you."

"Then I won't run away," said Pinocchio. But as Pinocchio told that lie, his nose started to grow.

Pinocchio had eaten nothing all day. He began to have a

strange feeling in his stomach.
He ran around the room looking
for food. He looked in cupboards.
"There must be at least a crust
of bread," thought Pinocchio.
But he could find nothing at all.

"You were right," cried
Pinocchio. "I should not have
run away from home. Then my
father would be here now. Oh!
It is dreadful to be hungry."

Pinocchio left the house to
beg for food. It was a stormy
night. The wind was blowing.

The streets were dark. All the shops were closed.

At last Pinocchio went back home. He was afraid of the thunder. He was wet. He was tired and hungry. He sat down in front of the fireplace to dry his wet feet. Then he fell asleep.

Pinocchio awoke early the next morning. Someone was knocking on the door.

"Who is there?" Pinocchio asked, yawning and rubbing his eyes.

"It is I!" answered Geppetto.

Pinocchio jumped up and started for the door. He stumbled. He got up again. He fell flat on the floor.

"Please open the door," called Geppetto.

"Dear Papa, I cannot," cried Pinocchio. "My feet have been eaten."

"Who has eaten your feet?" asked Geppetto.

"The cat," Pinocchio replied. He had seen a cat playing with some shavings. He thought she had eaten his feet.

Geppetto climbed up the side of the house and came in through the window. He saw Pinocchio lying on the floor without any feet. Geppetto took Pinocchio up in his arms. "My poor little Pinocchio," he said. "Your feet have been burned."

"Oh, Papa," cried Pinocchio. "It was a terrible night. I went out to beg for something to eat. But I came home again wet, tired, and hungry. I sat down in front of the fire to dry my feet. I must have had them too close to the fire when I fell asleep. Now I have no feet. And I am still hungry."

Geppetto took three pears from his pocket. "These were for my breakfast," he said. "You may eat them."

Pinocchio was no longer hungry, but he began to cry again. He wanted a new pair of feet.

"Why should I make you new feet?" asked Geppetto. "Without feet you cannot run away from home again."

"I will always be good," sobbed Pinocchio.

"All boys promise that when they want something," replied Geppetto.

"I will even go to school and study," said Pinocchio.

Without saying another

word, Geppetto got out two small pieces of wood. In less than an hour the feet were finished.

"Close your eyes and go to sleep," Geppetto said to Pinocchio.

While Pinocchio was asleep, Geppetto fastened the feet on with a little glue.

As soon as Pinocchio awoke and saw his feet, he jumped down from the table. He leaped around the room. "Now I will go to school," said Pinocchio. "But first I need some clothes."

Geppetto was so poor that he did not have even a penny. But he made Pinocchio some clothes and a cap from pretty wallpaper. Then he stuck a feather in the cap.

Pinocchio ran to look at himself in a pail of water. He was so pleased with how he looked that he strutted all around the room. "I look just like a gentleman," said Pinocchio proudly.

"You do look fine," said Geppetto. "But always remember that fine clothes do not make a gentleman."

"I am dressed for school," said Pinocchio. "Now I need a book."

"I have no money to buy a book. Wait a minute," Geppetto added. He put on his old coat and ran out of the house.

Geppetto returned with a book. But his old coat was gone. The poor man had no coat, and it was snowing outside.

"Where is your coat, Papa?" asked Pinocchio.

"I sold it," replied Geppetto.

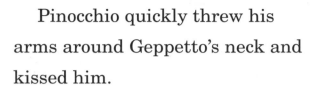

Pinocchio quickly threw his arms around Geppetto's neck and kissed him.

As soon as it stopped snowing, Pinocchio left for school.

"Today I shall learn to read," he thought. "Tomorrow I shall learn to write. The next day I shall do arithmetic. Then I shall be able to earn a lot of money. I will buy a new coat for Papa—a coat with gold buttons."

Suddenly Pinocchio stopped. He thought he heard music. He listened for a few moments.

At last Pinocchio decided, "Today I shall find out what the music is. Tomorrow I shall go to school."

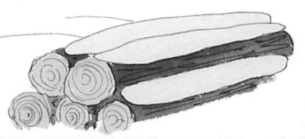

Pinocchio ran on and on. Soon he was in the middle of a crowd. "What is this place?" he asked a boy beside him.

"Read the sign," said the boy. "Then you will know."

"But I don't know how to read," Pinocchio said.

"Then you should be in school," replied the boy.

"How much does it cost?" asked Pinocchio.

"Twenty-five cents," said the boy.

Pinocchio felt very sad. He did not have any money.

"I will sell my school book for twenty-five cents!" Pinocchio cried.

"I will buy it," called out a man.

So the book was sold. Poor Geppetto was at home shivering. He had sold his only coat to buy the book. And Pinocchio didn't even go to school!

When Pinocchio left the puppet show, he saw a coach full of boys. The coach was drawn by donkeys. They were taking the boys to Playland.

"Come to Playland!" called a bad boy named Lampwick.

"I *was* going to school," said Pinocchio. Then he remembered that he didn't have a book. "Well, maybe I could go to Playland first—just for a little while."

Pinocchio and Lampwick played every day at
Playland. All day long they played. One day
Pinocchio noticed that Lampwick's ears were
growing longer. Then he began to grow a tail.
Pinocchio tried to tell Lampwick, but he only
laughed. "Hee-Haw! Hee-Haw!"

Pinocchio felt his own ears. They were long and pointed. He also had a tail! "The cricket was right," thought Pinocchio. "He said I would be a donkey if I didn't go to school. This must be what happens to lazy boys."

Pinocchio and Lampwick were taken to market and sold. A farmer bought Lampwick.

Pinocchio was sold to a circus. He learned to bow, to jump through hoops, and to do other tricks. Poor Pinocchio! He had a hard struggle. But everyone loved **Pinocchio, The Daring Donkey.**

Then one night Pinocchio fell. He could no longer do tricks, so his master sold him.

The buyer took the little donkey to the seashore. He pushed him into the sea. He wanted Pinocchio's donkey skin to make a drum.

Pinocchio swam fast. He got away from the man, but now he was being chased by a huge fish. The fish took a BIG drink of water. He swallowed poor Pinocchio!

It was so dark! Pinocchio
could hear nothing except a
roar—the sound of the fish
breathing.

Then Pinocchio saw a
light far, far away. He hurried toward it. He found a
little table. A candle was
stuck in a bottle on top of
it. Seated at the table was
an old man. He was eating
some little fish.

"Papa!" cried Pinocchio.
"Oh, my dear Papa! I will
never leave you again."

Pinocchio picked up the
candle. He started walking
toward the mouth of the big fish. "Come on,
Papa," he said. "We must get out of here."

Pinocchio and Geppetto walked for a long time. At last they could see the moon and the stars. They were in the throat of the big fish.

"The fish is asleep," whispered Pinocchio. "We shall soon be outside." Just then the fish felt something tickle his throat. "Ah-choo!"

The candle was blown out. Pinocchio and Geppetto were thrown back into the fish's belly.

"We are lost," cried the old man.

"Take hold of my hand," Pinocchio said. "Be careful not to slip."

Pinocchio and Geppetto came again to the throat of the fish. They climbed up to the tongue. They tiptoed past the teeth. Then they were out in the fresh air.

The old man and Pinocchio slid quietly into the water. Geppetto could not swim. He held onto Pinocchio, and after a long time they reached the shore. Pinocchio was very tired, but he found a place for Geppetto to rest. He made a nice bed of straw.

"Now I will find a glass of warm milk for you," Pinocchio whispered to Geppetto.

As Pinocchio was walking along, his tail disappeared. His ears were not long and pointed any more. But Pinocchio did not even notice. He was thinking only of his poor papa.

Pinocchio ran up to a farmer. "Will you please give me a glass of milk?" cried Pinocchio. "I have no money."

"Do you know how to draw water from a well?" asked the farmer.

"I can try," Pinocchio replied. "I will do anything for my papa."

"Then draw one hundred bucketfuls and I will give you a glass of milk."

Pinocchio worked hard. He had never felt so tired in all his life.

"I have a little donkey that usually draws water for me," said the farmer. "He is sick today."

Pinocchio carried water to the donkey. "Who are you?" Pinocchio asked in donkey language.

The donkey opened his eyes and said, "I am Lampwick." Then he closed his eyes again.

"Oh, my poor Lampwick," said Pinocchio.

"That donkey is not worth much," said the farmer. "Why do you care for him?"

"I went to school with him," replied Pinocchio. "At least I should have gone to school with him."

"You went to school with donkeys?" laughed the farmer.

Pinocchio was so ashamed! He took the glass of milk and quickly returned to Geppetto.

Every day Pinocchio drew water for the

farmer. He was given only a little milk each day. He also learned to make straw mats. He sold the mats to earn a little money. And every night he studied reading, writing, and arithmetic.

Pinocchio worked hard. He studied hard. He was kind to others and told the truth. He became less and less like a wooden puppet. One morning Pinocchio woke up and he was a real boy! He even had new clothes.

"Papa! Papa!" cried Pinocchio as he put his hands into his pockets. "Look at me!"

Geppetto had changed, too. He looked young again. "When bad boys become good," said Geppetto, "everything becomes better."

—*Adapted from C. Collodi*

A wise son maketh a glad father.

—*Proverbs 10:1*

Think about it:

Why did Pinocchio's tail disappear?

Making the Best of It

"What a dreary day this is!" said old Gray
Goose to Mrs. Brown Hen. They stood at the
henhouse window and watched the snow falling
outside. Every corner of the farmyard was turn-
ing white.

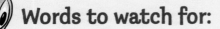

Words to watch for:

| alone | about | almost | appeared |
| became | enjoy | until | unhappy |

"Yes, indeed," answered Mrs. Brown Hen. "I would almost be willing to be made into chicken pie on a day like this."

A duck nearby said, "I am very hungry."

A group of speckled hens standing huddled together added, "And we are very thirsty!"

The farmer's boy usually fed them each day. Today he had given them nothing to eat or drink. As hour after hour went by, the animals became very

cross and unhappy. The cold winter wind howled around the henhouse, and they felt all alone.

Now, White Rooster was not like the others. He appeared to be quite happy as usual. No other animal in the farmyard ever seemed as jolly as White Rooster. He crowed just as loudly in stormy weather as he did in fair weather.

"Well," said White Rooster as he looked around the henhouse. "You all seem to be down in the dumps today." No one answered.

This was too much for White Rooster. He stood first on one foot and then on the other. He turned his head from side to side. Then he said, "If anyone looked in here right now, he would think we were surrounded by hungry foxes."

One of the little bantam roosters hopped down from his perch. He strutted over to White Rooster and said, "When we are full we are lively enough. When we are starving it is a wonder that we can hold our heads up at all. If I ever see that farmer's boy again, I'll peck his foot—I will, I will."

"You won't see the farmer's boy until he feeds us," replied White Rooster. "Then you'll be busy pecking the corn—not him."

"Oh, don't talk about a peck of corn," squawked Mrs. Brown Hen.

"Mrs. Brown Hen," said White Rooster as he bowed politely, "I am hungry, too. Your problem is my problem. It could be worse. We could be on our way to market in a box.

"We may not have enough to eat today. But we do have room enough to stretch our wings."

"That is true," answered Mrs. Brown Hen.

So all the animals in the henhouse stretched their wings and cleaned their feathers. They began to look a little happier.

"Now then," crowed White Rooster, "let's have a little music. That will cheer us up and help the hours pass. We will sing a merry song.

"Would you be so kind as to start a lively tune for us, Mrs. Brown Hen?"

Mrs. Brown Hen shook herself proudly. She tossed her head back and began, "Cut-cut-cut-ca-*dah*-cut." In no time at all everyone in the henhouse had joined her.

The cows, sheep, and horses were not far away. When they heard the happy voices in the henhouse, they, too, joined in the merry song. The pigs did their best to squeal louder than all the rest.

The animal chorus got louder and louder as each group tried a little harder.

All the animals were so happy that they forgot they were hungry.

All at once the door of the henhouse burst
open, and in marched three little children. Each
child was carrying a dish full of steaming
chicken food.

"Don't stop," laughed the little girl. "We enjoy your music." She was wrapped up in her coat and scarf. Her sweet little face could hardly be seen.

"We were so lonesome," she continued, "that we didn't know what to do. When we heard all of you singing, we laughed and laughed.

"We went to tell Jack, the farmer's boy, about you. He was lonesome, too. You see, Jack is sick with a sore throat.

"That's when Jack told us about you. 'Those poor animals!' he said. 'They haven't had anything to eat or drink.' "

"Cock-a-doodle-doo!" crowed White Rooster. "All this comes from making the best of things. Cock-a-doodle-doo!" And nobody asked him to stop crowing.

—*Adapted*

Think about it:

What is the title of this story? Do you think it fits the story? Why?

Cock-Crow

Cocks crow in the morn
    To tell us to rise,
And he who lies late
    Will never be wise.

For early to bed
    And early to rise,
Is the way to be healthy
    And wealthy and wise.

Time

How many seconds in a minute?

 Sixty, and no more in it.

How many minutes in an hour?

 Sixty, for sun and shower.

How many hours in a day?

 Twenty-four, for work and play.

How many days in a week?

 Seven, both to hear and speak.

Suppose

Suppose you're dressed for walking,
   And the rain comes pouring down.
Will it clear off any sooner
   Because you scold and frown?
And wouldn't it be nicer
   For you to smile than pout,
And so make sunshine in the house
   When there is none without?

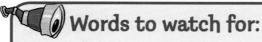

Suppose your task, my little man,

    Is very hard to get.

Will it make it any easier

    For you to sit and fret?

And wouldn't it be wiser

    Than waiting like a dunce

To go to work in earnest

    And learn the thing at once?

Suppose, my little lady,
  Your doll should break her head.
Could you make it whole by crying
  Till your eyes and nose are red?
And wouldn't it be pleasanter
  To treat it as a joke,
And say you're glad 'twas Dolly's
  And not your head that broke?

—*Phoebe Cary*

Think about it:

How is this poem like the story "Making the Best of It"?

The Lost Camel

A man from the East with great wisdom was once traveling in the desert. He met a group of merchants. The merchants traveled around selling things.

"We have lost one of our camels," the merchants said to the wise man. "Have you seen him?"

Words to watch for:

touched   search   merchants

"Was your camel blind in his right eye?" asked the wise man.

"Yes," said the merchants.

"Was he lame in one foot?" asked the wise man.

"Yes, he was," said the merchants.

"Did he have a front tooth missing?" asked the wise man.

"Yes, he did," replied the merchants.

"Was he loaded with wheat on one side and with honey on the other?" the wise man asked.

"Yes, he was! Where did you see our camel?" asked the merchants.

"I have not seen your camel," said the wise man.

The merchants were very angry. "You must have seen him. You know all about him. Have you taken our jewels and our money from his load?"

"No," said the wise man. "I have not seen your camel, your jewels, or your money."

The merchants did not believe the wise man. They took him to the judge. After they had told their story, the judge asked the wise man some questions.

"How did you know that the camel was blind in his right eye?" asked the judge.

The wise man replied, "I knew the camel was blind in his right eye because he had eaten grass on only one side of the path."

"How did you know that he was lame in one foot?" asked the judge.

"I saw that the print of one left foot was fainter than the others," said the wise man.

"How did you know that he was missing one tooth?" asked the judge.

"Wherever the camel had eaten, a small tuft of grass was left untouched in every bunch," said the wise man.

"Now," said the judge, "tell me how you could tell what the camel was carrying."

The wise man replied, "I watched busy ants on one side and flies on the other side. Then I knew that the camel was loaded with wheat and honey. I also knew that the camel had strayed away. There were no footprints before or behind the camel's footprints."

"You are indeed a wise man," said the judge. "I think you are also an honest man."

Then he said to the merchants, "Go and search for your camel."

The merchants did look for their camel. They found him not far away—and his load had not been touched!

—*An old legend*

How much better is it to get wisdom than gold! —*Proverbs 16:16*

Who?

Who gave the air,
    And made the sky?
Who formed the bird
    That soars on high?
Who taught its wings
    The way to fly?
    'Tis God.

Twinkle, Twinkle, Little Star

Twinkle, twinkle, little star,
How I wonder what you are.
Up above the world so high
Like a diamond in the sky.
Twinkle, twinkle, little star,
How I wonder what you are!

Rollie

Once there was a young rabbit named Rollie. Rollie was a happy rabbit. He had a father who worked hard. He had a mother who made him good meals. And he had four sweet brothers and sisters.

Words to watch for:

full	bushes	young	enough
come	mother	brother	company

But Rollie had a problem—Rollie *was* a problem. Whenever Mother or Father Rabbit told Rollie to do something, he forgot. Whenever they told Rollie not to do something, he would do it.

It made Rollie sad that he was a problem. It made Mother and Father Rabbit sad. And it made Rollie's brothers and sisters sad.

Mother and Father Rabbit tried to help Rollie learn to listen. They would pick up Rollie's long, floppy ears and speak right into them. But Rollie still forgot.

One day Rollie woke up and jumped out of bed. Company was coming! He was going on a picnic with his friends. He worked as fast as he could.

Rollie ran to his mother. She was packing a basket of food for Rollie. There was a jar filled with carrots, a bowl of lettuce, and a carrot cake.

As Rollie grabbed his hat, Mother Rabbit said, "Rollie, you will need to walk. Do not run with the basket. If you fall down, you might spill everything. Then you and your friends will not have enough food."

Rollie looked out the door. "Here they come!" he yelled. He gave his mother a kiss. Then he grabbed the basket, and out the door he skipped.

Rollie and his friends walked down the path into the woods. The spot for the picnic had already been chosen. In about five minutes they would be there.

Molly Mouse and Nibbles Chipmunk began to run ahead. They wanted to be the first ones to the picnic spot.

Just then Timothy Turtle crawled onto the path. "Where is everyone going?"

Rollie stopped. "Oh, hi, Timothy Turtle. We're going on a picnic. Would you like to come along? We will have to hurry, or we'll be late."

Rollie started to run. He tripped over a rock, and the basket went flying.

There lay Rollie on the ground. The basket was upside down in the bushes.

"Oh, dear!" cried Rollie. "My mother said not to run, and I forgot! Now what will I do?"

Timothy Turtle crawled over to see if Rollie was hurt. "You need to listen better," he said.

"I do listen," said Rollie, "but I still forget."

"Have you tried thinking about what you are told?" asked Timothy Turtle.

"I once had the same problem. I listened, but I did not think. I was in too much of a hurry. But one day I did not have anything else to do. When my mother told me something, I took time to think about it. And I did not forget what she said. Why not try it?" asked Timothy Turtle. And on down the road he crawled.

Rollie picked himself up. Then he picked up his basket. The food was all dirty. "We do not have enough food for a picnic," said Rollie. "I will have to go home."

When Rollie got home, he told his mother what had happened. He did not tell her what Timothy Turtle had said. But the next time Mother or Father Rabbit told Rollie something, he thought about what was said.

From that day on, Rollie's mother, father, sisters, and brothers were not sad any more. Rollie listened, thought, and did not forget.

—*Coletta Morrow*

Think about it:

What lesson did Rollie learn?

Sun and Rain

Down falls the pleasant rain
 To water thirsty flowers;
Then shines the sun again
 To cheer this earth of ours.

If it were always rain,
 The flowers would soon be drowned;
If it were always sun,
 No flowers would then be found.

Part Four
Apples, Cherries, and Pets

A Pet Crow

A man had a pet crow named Blackie. He fed Blackie. He talked to Blackie. He even let Blackie fly wherever he wanted to go. "Caw, caw," called Blackie as he flew about the lawn.

One autumn day Blackie flew far away from home. He got caught in a rainstorm. His feathers got so wet that he could not fly.

A boy found Blackie and took him home with him. The boy clipped one of Blackie's wings so that he could not fly away.

"Please let me go home," cawed Blackie.

But the boy did not let Blackie go home. He kept Blackie shut up all winter.

At last spring came. The first time Blackie got out, he started for his old home. He could not fly, because his wing was clipped. He had to hop seven miles in the rain and mud.

It was just past sunrise when Blackie came close to his home. His hops became slower and slower. He was so tired that he was almost dead.

The man saw Blackie coming and ran to meet his pet. He picked Blackie up and carried him. He gave him some food and talked kindly to him.

Blackie was home! How happy he was. When Blackie's new feathers grew, he could even fly. But never again did Blackie fly far away from home.

—Adapted

A friend loveth at all times.

—Proverbs 17:17

Johnny Appleseed

One day Jonathan Chapman sat thinking. As a young man he wanted to do something to help others. Suddenly he smiled.

He clapped his hands with boyish glee,
And said to himself, "There's a work for me!"

Words to watch for:

Creator   labored   beggar   vision

Poetry quoted throughout this story is from "Appleseed John" by Lydia Maria Child.

After that Johnny worked early. He worked late. He labored day and night. He did anything he could find to do.

> *He took ripe apples in pay for chores*
> *And carefully cut out all the cores.*

Johnny put each and every core into a bag.

> *He filled a bag full, then wandered away,*
> *And no man saw him for many a day.*

> *He traveled over the prairies wide,*
> *But he stopped now and then, and the bag*
>   *untied.*

Wherever he stopped, he planted apple seeds. He was an American pioneer. He had a vision of apple orchards across the land. As the years passed, he became known as Johnny Appleseed.

Sometimes Johnny Appleseed worked at farm-houses for food and clothes. He seldom wore shoes. Even during the cold winters he would be barefooted. Extra clothes or shoes were sometimes given to him, but he often gave them to someone in need. When his hat wore out, he carried his cooking pot on his head.

What a strange sight was Johnny Appleseed! He looked like a beggar. But the men, women, and children were always glad to see him.

He tossed up the babies and joined the boys
In making a game of fun and noise.

At night everyone sat around the fire. They listened to Johnny Appleseed sing songs and hymns. They listened to him tell stories. The children loved to hear the stories from the Bible. Then Johnny Appleseed told how the owls hooted. He told how the prairie dogs barked when he slept on the ground alone.

Johnny Appleseed made many friends. Everyone was glad when he came, and they wanted him to stay a long time.

But he always said, "I have something to do,
And I must go on and carry it through."

Then off he went, dressed in his old, ragged clothes. He carried with him his sack filled with apple seeds and his Bible.

Sometimes Johnny Appleseed met Indians. He was their friend, too. He often stayed with them at night. They also shared their food with him.

Johnny Appleseed walked alone through the wilderness, but he was not lonely. He loved the wild flowers and trees. He loved their Creator. He made friends with the animals. He called them God's creatures. He learned to imitate the call of many birds and animals.

Whenever he ran out of seeds, he went back for more. Then he took care of his seedlings and young saplings. But Johnny Appleseed always went west again carrying his apple seeds and his Bible.

As the years passed, Johnny Appleseed grew older. His steps became slower and slower.

Poor Johnny was bended nearly double
With years of toil, and care, and trouble.

But his large old heart still felt the need
Of doing for others some kindly deed.

Johnny Appleseed believed God's Word, "I have planted . . . but God giveth the increase."

When he was an old, old man, Jonathan Chapman died. But Johnny Appleseed is still

remembered. He is remembered because of the apple trees that blossom across the land.

The little seeds his hands had spread
Became ripe apples when he was dead.

—*Adapted*

Think about it:

Would you have liked to have known Johnny Appleseed? Why?

The Little Star

"I cannot do much," said a little star,
  "To make the dark world bright.
My silver beams cannot struggle far
  Through the folding gloom of night;
For I'm only a part of God's great plan,
  But I'll cheerfully do the best I can."

Cherries or Sparrows?

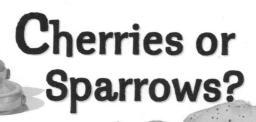

There was once a king who was very fond of cherries. The sparrows in his garden pecked nearly all of the ripe fruit. One day almost every cherry in his dish had been marked by a sparrow's beak.

This made the king very angry. "Kill all the sparrows!" he ordered.

 Words to watch for:

cherry   cherries   sparrow

One day the wise men told the king, "The insects are eating the biggest and best cherries."

At the end of two years, there were not many cherries left on the branches. There was only a little fruit of any kind.

The wise men came to the king again. "There are only a few sparrows left in the country. There are not enough to eat the insects. The insects are eating all of the fruit. The sparrows were very helpful—they ate the insects, but they ate so little of the fruit."

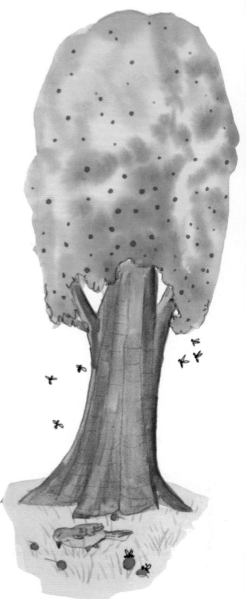

Since the king wanted more cherries to eat,
he gave new orders. "Kill no more sparrows," he
said. "They may eat a little of the fruit which
they save for others."

—*Adapted*

The Lord by wisdom hath founded the
earth; by understanding hath He estab-
lished the heavens.   —*Proverbs 3:19*

Freddie and the Cherry Tree

Freddie saw some fine ripe cherries
   Hanging on a cherry tree.
And he said, "You pretty cherries,
   Will you not come down to me?"

"Thank you kindly," said a cherry;
   "We would rather stay up here.
If we dared to drop this morning,
   You would eat us up, I fear."

One, the finest of the cherries,
   Dangled from a slender twig.
"You are beautiful," said Freddie,
   "Red and ripe, and oh, how big!"

"Catch me," called the cherry. "Catch me,
    Little mister, if you can."
"I would catch you soon," said Freddie,
    "If I were a grown-up man."

Freddie jumped and tried to reach it,
    Standing high upon his toes.
But the cherry bobbed about,
    And laughed, and tickled Freddie's nose.

"Never mind," said little Freddie,
    "I shall have them when it's right."
But a blackbird whistled boldly,
    "I shall eat them all tonight."

The Kitten That Wanted to Be a Birthday Present

One rainy day a bunny went hopping through the woods. The ground was covered with water, but Benjamin Bunny did not mind. He had thick, warm fur.

All at once Benjamin Bunny stopped. He sat up and listened with his long ears. He heard, "Mew, mew!"

Words to watch for:

certain   motion   confusion   compassion

Benjamin Bunny was afraid.
"What was that noise?" he asked.
Just then he heard the cry again, "Mew,
mew!"

Benjamin Bunny hopped over a log. He
saw a little kitten in a puddle of water.

"Mew, mew," cried the little kitten.

Benjamin Bunny had never seen a kitten before, because kittens do not live
in the woods. "What is the matter?"
asked Benjamin Bunny. "I heard you
calling. I hopped over to see what
was the trouble."

"Oh, please," said the little kitten,
I am wet and cold. How do you go so
fast?"

"I hop," said Benjamin Bunny. "Shall I help you get home?"

"Oh," replied the little kitten, "I have no home."

"What do you mean?" asked Benjamin Bunny. "I thought everyone had a home."

"I used to have a home," said the little kitten. "I lived in a barn with my mother and brothers. One day there was a big wind. Pieces of the barn fell down around us. My mother told us to run. And I ran. When I stopped, I could not find my mother."

"That is sad," said Benjamin Bunny with compassion. "What are you going to do?"

"I want to be a birthday present," said the little kitten.

"A birthday present!" replied Benjamin Bunny. "What kind of an animal is that?"

"I'm not quite certain," said the little kitten. "But my grandmother was one. She said that if you are a birthday present, you have someone to love you. You have enough to eat. You have a warm place to sleep. And you are so happy that you purr."

"How do you purr?" asked Benjamin Bunny.

"I don't know," said the little kitten. "I have tried many times, but I have not been able to do it yet."

"Come with me," Benjamin Bunny said. "Maybe we can find someone who can tell us about birthday presents."

Benjamin Bunny led the way through the woods. Soon they met two squirrels. "Where are you going?" asked Chat and Chatter.

"We are trying to find someone who knows about birthday presents," said Benjamin Bunny.

"Oh," cried Chatter. "The bears told me about birthdays."

Off went the little kitten, Benjamin Bunny, Chat, and Chatter to visit the bears. When they arrived, Benjamin Bunny said, "This kitten wants to be a birthday present. Do you know about birthday presents?"

"Oh, we know all about them," said Papa Bear. "We have a friend who lives in a cabin on the other side of the woods. Each year he makes things or buys things. He wraps them in pretty paper." Papa Bear went through the motions of wrapping a present.

"He calls them birthday presents," added Mama Bear. "When we were looking for food early this week, we came near the cabin. We saw the man and his wife talking. We heard them say that they still needed a present for their little girl."

"Maybe the little girl would like a kitten for a birthday present," said Baby Bear.

"Will you show us where to go?" asked Chatter.

"We will be glad to show you," said the three bears. So off went the animals through the woods.

Early that evening the animals arrived at the cabin. As they sat down to rest, they thought of a plan. "Little kitten, you go up to the porch and sit down. We will make some noise so that the man will come to the door. Then he will see you. If he wants you for a birthday present, he will take you inside."

The little kitten said good-bye to her new friends. "If I get to stay here," she said, "please come to visit me." Then the little kitten turned and walked up to the porch.

There was much confusion as the bears growled and the squirrels chattered.

Just as the kitten sat down by the door, the man opened it. What a surprise he had when he saw the kitten sitting on the porch!

"Well, well," said the man. "Where did you come from?" The man picked up the little kitten. He stepped down from the porch to look around, but he saw nothing. Then he went into the house and closed the door.

The man laid the little kitten on a rug in front of a warm fire. The man's wife got her a dish of warm milk. The little kitten drank the warm milk. Then she curled up on the rug in front of the fire and went to sleep.

When the little kitten opened her eyes, she was still on the rug. Another dish of milk was beside her. The door behind her opened. In ran a sweet little girl. She stooped over and picked up the little kitten.

"Oh, you dear, dear kitty. Are you my birthday present?" she asked as she gave the little kitten a hug.

The kitten looked up into the little girl's face. It was even better to be a birthday present than she had thought. And then, without knowing what she was doing, the little kitten began to purr.

—*Adapted*

A merry heart maketh a cheerful countenance.　　　　　*—Proverbs 15:13*

Think about it:

Why was the kitten in the woods? What did she want to do to make the best of her situation? How did the other animals help her?

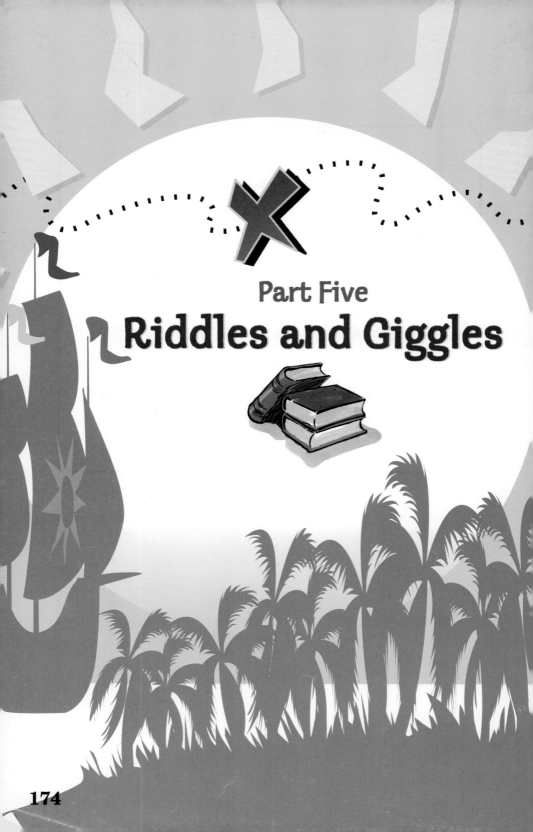

Part Five
Riddles and Giggles

Do You Know?

(Turn the page upside-down to find the answers!)

1 What can fill
   A great big house,
Yet still weigh less
   Than a tiny mouse?

2 What key is too large to carry?

(1) smoke, (2) a donkey

3 When is a boy most like a bear?

4 What runs all around the pasture, yet never once moves?

5 What makes more noise than a squealing pig caught under a gate?

(3) when he is barefooted, (4) the fence, (5) two squealing pigs caught under a gate

6. What kind of ears do engines have?

7. What is the difference between an old penny and a new dime?

8. When can your pocket be empty and still have something in it?

9 What can you hold in your left hand that you can never hold in your right hand?

10 You can find me one time in every minute, two times in every moment, yet never find me in one hundred years. What am I?

11 What gets wetter the more it dries?

(9) your right elbow, (10) the letter m, (11) a towel

178

12 Which side of a pie is the left side?

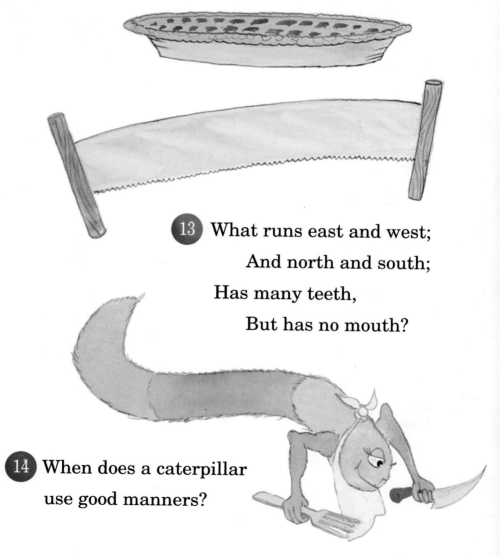

13 What runs east and west;
And north and south;
Has many teeth,
But has no mouth?

14 When does a caterpillar
use good manners?

(12) the side that isn't eaten, (13) a saw, (14) when he turns over a new leaf

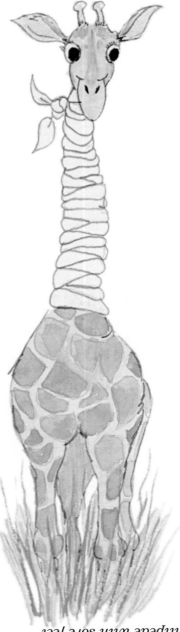

15 How could you fall from a hundred-foot ladder and not get hurt?

16 What is worse than a giraffe with a sore throat?

(15) *fall from the bottom rung.* (16) *a centipede with sore feet*

17 Where are kings usually crowned?

18 What is the longest word in the dictionary?

19 If you drop a pea into the sea, what will it become?

Simple Simon

Simple Simon met a pie man,
    Going to the fair.
Says Simple Simon to the pie man,
    "Let me taste your ware."

Says the pie man to Simple Simon,
    "Show me first your penny."
Says Simple Simon to the pie man,
    "Indeed, I have not any."

A Pretty Little Thing

I'm a pretty little thing,
  Always coming with the spring;
In the meadows green I'm found,
  Peeping just above the ground.
And my stalk is covered, flat,
  With a white and yellow hat.

Little children, when you pass
  Lightly o'er the tender grass,
Step aside and do not tread
  On my meek and lowly head;
For I always seem to say,
  "Chilly winter's gone away."

What am I?

A daisy

A Cunning Little Thing

I'm a cunning little thing,
  Coming also with the spring.
Near the daisy I am found,
  Standing straight above the ground;
And my head is covered flat
  With a glossy, yellow hat.

Little children, when you pass
  Through the tall and waving grass,
Do not pluck, but gently tread
  Near my low and mossy bed;
For I always seem to say,
  "Milk and butter fresh today."

What am I?

A buttercup

184

Five Little Chicks

Said the first little chick
   With a quick little squirm,
"Oh, I wish I could find
   A fat little worm!"

Said the next little chick
   With an odd little shrug,
"Oh, I wish I could find
   A good little bug!"

Said the third little chick
   With a sharp little squeal,
"Oh, I wish I could find
   Some nice yellow meal!"

Said the fourth little chick
  With a shake of his head,
"Oh, I wish I could find
  A small crumb of bread!"

Said the fifth little chick
  As she looked all around,
"Oh, I wish I could find
  Any food on the ground!"

"Now, see here," said their mother
  From the green garden patch,
"If you want any breakfast,
  You must all come and scratch!"

—An Old Verse

A Funny Dream

Late last night as I lay in my bed,
    I had such a funny dream.
Something looked so very good—
    A little house made of ice cream.
A lot of animals passed that way—
    A hawk, a fawn, a seal.
They all were licking that little house.
    Oh! What a yummy meal!

Then the sun began to shine—
    The little house started to thaw.
All the animals ran right home
    And came back with a straw!

—*Coletta Morrow*

There was . . .

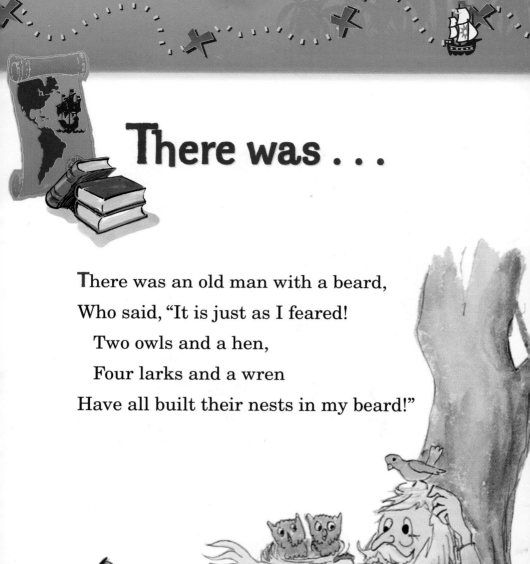

There was an old man with a beard,
Who said, "It is just as I feared!
  Two owls and a hen,
  Four larks and a wren
Have all built their nests in my beard!"

There was a young boy who said, "See
The beautiful bluebird in that tree!"
    When they asked, "Is it small?"
    He replied, "Not at all.
It is four times as big as the tree!"

There was a young lady whose chin
Resembled the point of a pin;
    So she had it made sharp,
    And purchased a harp,
And played several tunes with her chin.

A little girl once asked, "Why
    Can't I look in my ear with my eye?
        If I give my mind to it,
        I'm sure I can do it.
    You never can tell till you try!"

Twenty Froggies

Twenty froggies went to school
Down beside a rushy pool,
Twenty little coats of green,
Twenty vests all white and clean.

"We must be on time," said they.
"First we study, then we play;
That is how we keep the rule,
When we froggies go to school."

Master Bullfrog, grave and stern,
Called the classes in their turn;
Taught them how to nobly strive,
Likewise how to leap and dive.

From his seat upon the log,
He showed them how to say, "Ker-chog!"
Also how to dodge a blow
From the sticks that bad boys throw.

Twenty froggies grew up fast;
Bullfrogs they became at last.
Not one dunce among the lot,
Not one lesson they forgot.

Polished in a high degree,
As each froggie ought to be,
Now they sit on other logs,
Teaching other little frogs.

—*An Old Verse*

Grasshopper Green

Grasshopper Green is a comical chap;
   He lives on the best of fare.
Bright little trousers, jacket, and cap,
   These are his summer wear.

Out in the meadow he loves to go,
   Playing away in the sun;
It's hopperty, skipperty, high and low,
   Summer's the time for fun!